Below, and throughout this sticker book, you can see some of the creatures that lived at this time. Look at your sticker sheet and match the dinosaurs, then stick them on to the big picture!

Peteinosaurus

Placerias

Coelophysis

Postosuchus

Plateosaurus

Giants on the loose

155 million years ago — in the Jurassic Period —
as the Earth gets wetter and warmer, the dinosaurs flourish…

Anurognathus

Brachiosaurus

Allosaurus

Stegosaurus

Lurking in the sea

The vast, warm Jurassic seas are filled with the most amazing and mysterious creatures…

Ammonite

Cryptoclidus

Ophthalmosaurus

Hybodus shark

Liopleurodon

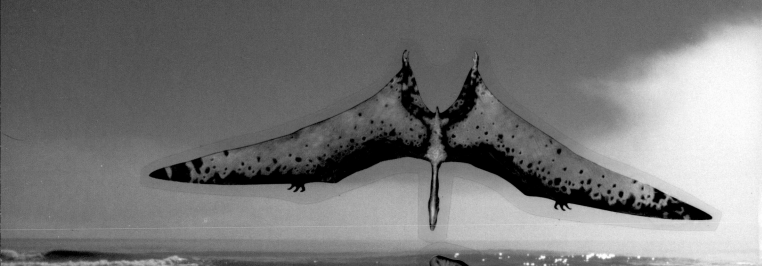

Looming in the sky

Far above the dinosaurs, flying reptiles of all sizes soar through the ancient skies…

Rhamphorhynchus
(Jurassic Period)

Quetzalcoatlus
(Cretaceous Period)

Tapejara
(Cretaceous Period)